S0-AHS-697

THE EASTER STORY

Mi
16
Mck E

0|57

The Easter Story

As Retold by

Felix R. McKnight

HENRY HOLT AND COMPANY, INC., NEW YORK

Copyright, 1953, by Henry Holt and Company, Inc.

All rights reserved, including the right to reproduce

this book or portions thereof in any form.

Reprinted with the permission of the Dallas *Morning News.*

First Edition

Library of Congress Catalog Card Number: 53-5503

Printed in the United States of America

THE LIBRARY OF
GARRETT BIBLICAL INSTITUTE
EVANSTON, ILLINOIS

PZ7
.M159t
1953

PALM SUNDAY:

Day of Triumph

The thirty-three-year-old son of a carpenter rode triumphantly astride a restless colt through Jerusalem's gates nearly 1,925 years ago today—acclaimed as the prophesied Messiah.

Thousands of the faithful hurried along the streets tossing their mantles and palm branches on the rough stones before the young, sad-eyed Jesus of Nazareth, crying out:

"Hosanna to the Son of David!"

The day was magnificent in its beauty. It was April and spring. The Sabbath sun's brilliance sparkled across vineyards and orchards. Velvety blue skies canopied the countryside.

Only a few hours before Jesus had gathered around Him on the nearby Mount of Olives, at Bethphage village, His twelve Disciples. He told them of His fate—that He was to be outraged, struck and spit upon and finally put to death.

220233

It seemed incredible to His followers. But Jesus calmed them. Death was to be the promise of a second, and greater, life and His Passion was to insure eternal freedom of man.

So with a beckoning gesture He started His triumphal march upon Jerusalem—a condemned man who thrice had escaped death but who now chose it to save mankind.

The crowd swelled as a mad river out of its banks as the procession neared Jerusalem. The faithful, caught in a great moment of hope, slashed palm branches and boughs of myrtle from the forests and waved them high.

The din grew and some feared a riot at the gates. The Pharisees, gathered to prepare the Sacrifice of the Passover, hurried to the scene and drew cloaks about troubled faces as they heard the rolling shout:

"Blessed be the King that cometh in the name of the Lord; peace in heaven and glory in the highest!"

The first Christian legion storming Jerusalem's gates irked the Pharisees and some cried out at this strange Jesus of Nazareth:

"Master, rebuke Thy disciples!"

But the answer withered them; rang like a challenge of war:

"If these should hold their peace, the stones would immediately cry out!"

Stones? The stones of dusty streets which had twice been hurled at Him in murder attempts. The desert stones which He had refused to turn into loaves of bread upon the dare of His enemy.

The issue was made. On He rode, the trace of a smile on His gentle face as He raised His head slightly to acknowledge the drumming Hosannas.

A tear dropped on His cheek. He was crying softly to Himself; not in self-pity; not for the suffering He would endure; not for the shame He knew He faced; not for the death that awaited Him a few days hence.

No, He sorrowed not for Himself, but for the poor souls who were about to perjure and compromise themselves at the altar of unbelief. Knowing that the Scripture must be fulfilled, that the prophecy must come to pass, He knew they would do just that.

Meanwhile, the Pharisees called hurried councils among the Chief Priests and Scribes to discuss the threat this carpenter's son had brought to their midst. The throngs that tearfully shouted at His heels disturbed them. He was a menace to be destroyed.

But Jesus, marching ironically in triumph to His doom, heard only the joyous shout that pounded over Jerusalem—even to the walls of the Temple on the hill; the Temple filled with sin:

"Hosanna to the Son of David!"

Tomorrow He would lash from the Temple of God the money-changers, the bankers, the venders who dared to invade the House of the Lord.

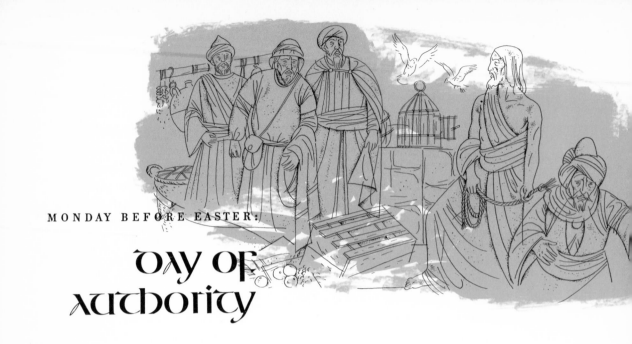

Day of Authority

Jesus of Nazareth strode up the dusty Jerusalem street to the Temple of God, flanked by His fervent followers.

On the hilltop the Temple beckoned in deceiving brilliance. But His gentle heart flamed into righteous indignation as He drew near. He saw what He had feared.

Sin had occupied the House of the Lord.

Greed was etched in the faces of the money-changers who ran dirty hands through bowls of silver and copper. Herdsmen hawked their wares in the filth of their flocks. Vendors shouted raucously beside their pigeon coops.

Oxen bellowed against a backdrop of bleating lambs. Against the din He stood in scorn and viewed it all. The house of prayer was now a house of Mammon, and money-changers cheated and lied and became the tools of priests.

No longer could He restrain His scorn. The gentlest of all men seized a knotted rope and lashed His way through the market place. He stung evil backs and upset benches of the money-changers. Copper and silver coins clattered to the floor and rolled away. Greedy men bawled in astonishment.

Herdsmen stampeded oxen and sheep through the Temple doors and vendors tumbled to the floor beside upset coops. The babble drew others from nearby courtyards and the clamor rose at the sight of this man cleansing the Temple of God.

He stood majestically brandishing His whip and with the last of the money-changers crawling from the Temple, loudly called after them:

"My house shall be called the house of prayer; but ye have made it a den of robbers and thieves!"

And suddenly the courts were cleared and there was peace.

Soon, in the new quiet of the Temple, there came the blind and the lame. Boys of the neighborhood, possibly choir boys, cautiously slipped in to see this man who had driven evil from holy halls.

The Chief Priests and Scribes of the Pharisees, drawn to the Temple by the act of Jesus of Nazareth, watched incredibly while He healed the afflicted. They frowned uncomfortably when little children cried and joyously shouted:

"Hosanna to the Son of David!"

Indignantly the Priests called out to Him:

"Do you hear what they say?"

And Jesus answered:

"Why are they saying this of me? Haven't you read in the Scriptures: 'You have drawn praise from the mouths of children and infants'?"

And that silenced the Pharisees. But it taunted them and it was that night that they banded together and conceived the bribing of a betrayer—and the cross. It was a delicate plot to plan, for the people had accepted Jesus as the

Messiah and hung upon His every word.

On that day Jesus, weary and faint of hunger, walked near Bethany. He saw a fig tree and sought to satisfy His hunger. But the tree was barren of fruit and He grew indignant. He spoke that no more fruit would grow on the tree.

Matthew reported the tree withered at once. John told that when they passed it the next day it had perished. But in any event it could not suffer His ire.

Jesus told His followers it was but a lesson—that men needed to realize a simple faith, a faith in God which rests on Him alone.

He was trying to tell them that the fig tree was like Jerusalem, which, with its foliage, was magnificent in its welcome on the day of His triumphant Sabbath entry. But, actually, it had not received Him, did not understand His visitation, and was as barren as the tree He had spurned.

And then He went to Bethany for a night of quiet.

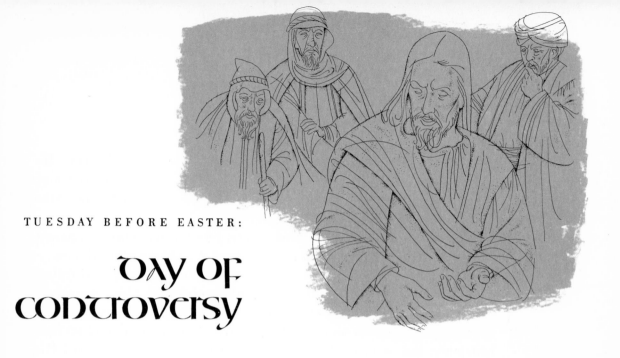

Day of Controversy

It was to be a bitter and full day for Jesus of Nazareth—the Tuesday before Easter, last day in His public ministry.

So with the dawn over Bethany He arose, gathered His disciples, and started for the Temple of God He had cleansed the day before.

Jerusalem was feverish.

It had heard in every house how Jesus drove the wicked from the House of the Lord. The poor rejoiced and left the alleys; leprous beggars lurched toward the Temple; craftsmen long suffering at the hands of the rich closed their shops.

The courts were overflowing as He walked in one of the Porches to begin His teaching. The lame and the poor watched imploringly. The multitude belonged to Jesus that day.

But He was not to be without enemies. In small groups the Pharisees and Scribes who plotted His death filtered into the courtyard. They were haughty sights. Sneering mouths, scorn in their eyes, tilted chins.

Jesus paused and awaited their attack. He knew why they had come. He knew their cunning. Soon one of them shouted:

"By what authority do you preach—and who gave this authority?"

Jesus' answer shamed them and the multitude was pleased.

"I would ask you a question. If you answer, I will tell you by what authority I do these things. The baptism of John—whence was it? From heaven or from men?"

The Pharisees were shaken. If they answered "from heaven" He would ask, "Why did you not believe him?" If they answered "from men" they would be stoned, for the people were persuaded John was a prophet. So they shamefully said:

"We know not."

And Jesus said:

"Neither will I tell you by what authority I do these things."

But again the Pharisees attempted cunning. One asked:

"Is it lawful to give tribute to Caesar? Why pay taxes?"

Jesus deliberated. To have said "no" would have been to command rebellion. To have said "yes" would have belied His own claim to Messiahship. But He knew well of their hypocrisy. He took a coin and said:

"What is Caesar's give to Caesar, and what is God's to God."

The Pharisees heard and marveled and left the temple. And the solution Jesus gave has settled for all time the principles underlying it.

Jesus paused for rest on nearby steps and watched the multitude cast money into the treasury. He saw a pauper widow give two mites, the smallest of coins, and knew that her sacrifice was the greatest of all. Their glances met and Jesus was pleased, although He did not speak.

Their silence was a tryst for heaven.

The day was long and Jesus was tired. He silenced the Sadducees when questioned on resurrection and then the Pharisees reappeared to plague Him on the law.

"What command is the greatest of the commandments?" they asked.

"You must love God with all your heart and all your soul and all your mind. There is a second. You must love your neighbor as yourself. There is none other commandment greater than these."

The evening came and Jesus wearied. He had told many parables and had attempted to correct many errors. It was then that He met the approach of the proselytes. Greeks who had married into Judaism. They wanted to become disciples of the Lord of Righteousness. They sent a messenger, Philip Bethsaida, accompanied by Andrew.

And Gentile converts were granted the right to worship and praise Christ, even as men of the Gentile world had paid homage to Him in the stable of Bethlehem.

Jesus said unto Philip and Andrew:

"The hour is come that the Son of man should be glorified. If any man serve me, let him follow me; and where I am there shall also my servant be. If any man serve me, him will the Father honor . . ."

And Jesus, perhaps the fullest day of His life ended—He had confounded the Pharisees and Scribes, He had foretold the destruction of Jerusalem and His own suffering on the cross—returned to the home of Lazarus in Bethany.

Day of Retirement

On Wednesday of His Passion week Jesus of Nazareth sought seclusion in the quiet of friendly Bethany homes. No record of events of this day in His life is known.

But wicked schemers, the troubled Pharisees and Scribes who feared the challenging power of the Son of David, met to plan details of His death.

To openly assassinate Him would bring down the plague of the people. Betrayal and crucifixion was the plan. The right moment had to be found.

To the court of the high priest, Caiaphas, went the plotters to counsel together. The Sanhedrin, supreme council of the capital's ruling chiefs, was crowded with priests who benefited from the Temple's merchandising, Scribes who tended the law, and Elders who represented the middle class.

Why did this group seek the death of Jesus?

Greed and personal interests were the underlying causes.

Intertwined in every business in Jerusalem, from the high to the low, was religion. The high priests were beneficiaries of tithes, taxes from Temple trading, food from sacrificial animals, and even from payments for first-born infants.

It was their privilege to take from herds and crops. Under the law even the bread on their tables came from Jews who were compelled to give the twenty-fourth part of the bread baked in their homes. They sold animals to be used in sacrificial offerings and formed secret partnerships with the money-changers.

Shamefully, the Temple of God became a bartering post around which was wrapped the very life of Jerusalem. Off the Temple lived the priests and the wealthy. Merchants depended upon the priests and the rich and the millions of pilgrims drawn from over the world to the tainted house of worship.

The poor existed from scraps dropped them by those who desecrated the Temple.

To challenge this violation of God's House came Jesus. His teachings substituted love of man for every mercenary scheme and threatened the continued existence of an infamous network.

Many attempts to trap Him with cunning questions had failed. Jerusalem was crowded with pilgrims for the Sacrifice of the Passover and tens of thousands were either listening to or hearing of His teachings. It troubled the Pharisees.

Only Nicodemus arose in the Sanhedrin to attempt defense of Jesus, but he was quieted by fearful shouts of others that if He were permitted to continue His teachings and gather great followings, the Romans would come in conquering strength and seize the nation.

Finally, the decision was made.

Jesus was to be seized before the Passover. But they were cowardly and still feared the wrath of the people. Many schemes were discussed for the actual murder, but it was decided against assassination on the day of the Passover "lest there be an uproar among the people."

But on the next day came a traitor to solve their problem.

Judas Iscariot, one of the Twelve Disciples, was to betray his Master for thirty pieces of silver—a modest sum for an avaricious man. It could not have been more than twenty dollars.

A small price for a man's life. And no one knows to this day the mystery of Judas Iscariot. We know only:

"Then entered Satan into Judas."

Day of Fellowship

Thirty pieces of silver were to be His doom before the day's end but Jesus of Nazareth tediously planned Maundy Thursday for last moments of fellowship and prayer with His Disciples.

Not many hours of life remained for Him. He was to be betrayed, given mock trial, and crucified before tomorrow's sunset.

So it was His wish that He should gather for the last time His Disciples, but no worldly goods were His and He had no home for such fellowship. He directed two Disciples to go into Jerusalem and follow a man bearing a pitcher and in his home they would dine.

Many men bore pitchers of water from Shiloh on that day but the Disciples followed the first they saw and it was as He said. Arrangements were made.

In the evening Jesus came and sat with His Disciples for the Lord's Supper and the Passover feast. It was the first day of unleavened bread. To prove His love for those He was soon to leave, Jesus stooped and washed the dusty feet of His Disciples. Protests arose but He said:

"Verily, verily I say unto you, a servant is not greater than his Lord; neither one that is sent greater than he that sent him. If ye know these things, blessed are ye if ye do them."

In His sadness He gave them a new commandment:

"Love one another, even as I have loved you. Greater love hath no man than this, that a man lay down his life for his friends . . ."

And He took the bread and broke it in prayer and gave it to them, saying:

"This is my body which is given for you. This do in remembrance of me."

And He took a cup and gave thanks and handed it to a Disciple.

"Drink ye all of it, for this is my blood of the new covenant which is shed for many . . ."

Great lines furrowed His face and He shocked His Disciples when he said:

"Verily, I say unto you that one of you will betray me."

The Disciples searched each other's faces and were sorrowful. They quickly pleaded to know the identity of the betrayer. Judas Iscariot, the thirty pieces of silver even then tightly wrapped on his person, said:

"Is it I, Lord?"

In answer, Jesus said:

"He it is for whom I shall dip the sop and give it to him."

And Jesus handed the sop to Judas Iscariot who fled into the night. Then He began His farewell conversation with the remaining Disciples who were of heavy heart:

"Let not your hearts be troubled. He who believes in God, believes also in Me. In my Father's house are many mansions; if it were not so I would have told you, for I go to prepare a place for you . . ."

The supper was ended and Jesus took with Him to the Garden of Geth-

semane Peter and James and John. He implored them to stay with Him and watch as He prayed. And He fell to the ground and cried to God:

"Father, all things are possible unto Thee; remove this cup from me!"

But only an angel appeared to give Him strength and in agony He prayed until blood and sweat coursed down His hot cheeks. He wearily arose and walked back to find the three Disciples lost in sleep. Not even His trusted friends could stand watch. He peered down at them and whispered:

"Sleep on now and take your rest. Behold, the hour is at hand and the Son of Man is betrayed into the hands of sinners."

Out of the shadows came Judas Iscariot in the light of lanterns. Swords rattled from scabbards of the motley rabble at his side. For thirty pieces of silver Judas Iscariot was to identify Jesus with a kiss.

So he walked straightway to Him and kissed His cheek. And Jesus said:

"Friend, betrayest thou the Son of Man with a kiss?"

The guards rushed forward and Simon Peter drew his sword and slashed an ear off the high priest's servant. Quickly Jesus said:

"Suffer ye then thus far."

And he touched the ear and healed it.

The Disciples left in confusion and fear and Jesus was led away to the house of Annas. His death sentence neared.

And Judas Iscariot fled into the night and hanged himself.

Day of Suffering

The day had come—mockery, insults, the fiction of a legal trial, boundless pain, betrayal, and, finally, death on the cross.

It was the day of suffering for Jesus Christ.

Dawn dispelled the dark on that Friday when Jesus, insulted and slapped in the home of Annas, was bound and led away to the palace of Caiaphas, high priest.

The day's first grief came when Peter, frightened and confused, stoutly denied in Caiaphas' courtyard that he was a Disciple of Christ; that he even knew Him. A distant cock crew and Peter gazed into Jesus' face and remembered His words:

"Before the cock crow twice thou shalt deny me thrice."

And Peter stumbled into the streets and wept bitterly, his face hidden in his cloak.

Into the crowded Sanhedrin Jesus, alone now and wrists bound with rope, was shoved to hear perjurers testify before Caiaphas. Two of them swore they had heard Him say in the Temple of God:

"I will destroy this temple that is made with hands and in three days I will build another made without hands."

But Jesus answered nothing; nothing until His own words condemned Him in the eyes of these evil schemers.

Caiaphas crooked a finger toward Him and asked:

"Art Thou the Son of God?"

And Jesus wrote His own death sentence:

"Ye say that I am. I say unto you, Hereafter shall ye see the Son of Man sitting on the right hand of power, and coming with the clouds of heaven."

Caiaphas triumphantly arose and tore his priestly garments in a deceitful show of rage, shouting:

"Ye have heard the blasphemy. What think ye?"

Death! Death! Death! The halls shook with their verdict.

Jesus, exhausted and blindfolded, dried blood clotted on His cheeks, stood with the guards. A passing Scribe spat upon Him. The rabble of servants and guards spitefully followed suit. And then they played blind man's buff—striking Him in His blindness and demanding that He identify His assailants without sight if He were really a prophet.

But they soon tired and Jesus was taken before Pontius Pilate, the Roman Governor, for confirmation of His sentence. The Pharisees falsely testified again and Pilate, unwilling to shoulder the responsibility, sent Him to Herod when He told him He was a Galilean. But Jesus was silent before Herod and the mob returned Him to Pilate for final decision.

Pilate, defending Jesus through hate of Caiaphas, not love, offered Barabbas, an assassin, in exchange for Jesus, but the throng still clamored for His death. So Pilate had Him stripped and arrayed in a purple garment and the soldiers in the courtyard placed a crown of thorns upon His head and a reed in His right hand.

And they spat upon Him and struck Him and mocked Him with:

"Hail, King of the Jews!"

And finally Pilate, fearful of the rising tumult, delivered Him unto the mob and washed his hands in water, saying:

"I am innocent of the blood of this man; see ye to it!"

Down the stony streets Jesus trudged, bearing His own cross. Two thieves followed, also doomed to crucifixion. Sobbing women, old men, dirty children followed the procession with cries of pity. But Jesus urged them not to weep for Him.

No longer could His strength hold. He fell to the street under His cross. He seemed dead; only gasps of breath showed life.

The Pharisees cast about in the crowd and picked one Simon to lift His cross that the procession might not be delayed. Outside the city's walls—capital punishment was illegal in the city itself—came the tragic, broken Jesus of Nazareth to a place called Golgotha, scene of the crucifixion.

Four soldiers readied Jesus and the two thieves. Ropes under His arms lifted Him to the cross and nails were driven into His hands and feet.

"Father, forgive them for they know not what they do . . ."

And one of the repentant thieves moaned in agony as Jesus comforted him.

"Today shalt thou be with me in paradise . . ."

Away from the howling men, fearful of it all, stood His mother, Mary. To John and Mary, Jesus whispered:

"Woman, behold thy son; son, behold thy mother!"

Midnight darkness came and the sun was obscured. Many fled in fear but some lingered. The parched lips moved again and at the ninth hour he said:

"My God, my God, why hast Thou forsaken me?"

Dust and blood coated His lips:

"I thirst . . ."

And a vile soldier dipped a reed in vinegar and brushed it to His mouth.

"It is finished . . ."

The body trembled and the lips parted in final agony:

"Father, into Thy hands I commend My spirit . . ."

And His head bowed and He gave up the ghost.

Suddenly, told Matthew, an earthquake struck and the Temple veil was torn from top to bottom. The earth shook and rocks were splintered. Tombs opened and bodies of saints were raised.

The people, in fear and awe, beat their breasts and cried:

"Truly, this was the Son of God!"

⌀ΛY OF
SOΓΓOW

Jesus Christ was dead. Man's freedom had been assured. Three crosses stood in Golgotha's darkness and only one of the two thieves breathed. The crowd had fled and in the shadows lingered only the three Marys.

To Pilate hurried those who demanded that the legs of the crucified be broken at once and the bodies buried before the setting of the sun and the beginning of the Passover.

It was ordered and as was the custom to hasten the death of the crucified, a soldier broke the legs of the living thief. Jesus was dead but John told that His side was pierced with a spear in a last gesture of cruelty.

Two notables of Jerusalem, Joseph of Arimathea and Nicodemus, went before the Pilate in the secrecy of darkness and asked for the body of Jesus. Pilate, mindful that some of the crucified lived many hours in agony, was astonished that He should be dead.

So he called before him the executioner and being assured of His death, gave unto Joseph the body of Jesus.

And Joseph took fine white linen bands and returned to Golgotha where he met Nicodemus, whose servant bore many pounds of myrrh. It was a dark and sinister night and the two set out flaming torches.

Slowly they lifted Him from the cross and placed His body on the knees of Mary, who had borne Him.

And then they carried Him to Joseph's nearby garden where a sepulcher had been hewn from rock for Joseph's family. It was to be the burial place of Jesus Christ.

Water was brought from the well and His body washed. The three Marys lifted from His bloodied brow the crown of thorns Pilate's soldiers had woven in mockery. They smoothed His long hair and tenderly washed His many wounds.

The pounds of myrrh were touched to His body and the winding linen was wrapped about Him and He was laid deep in a subterranean passageway intended for Joseph.

It was done and they kissed His forehead and departed.

But the three Marys lingered at the entrance to the sepulcher, where Joseph and Nicodemus had closed the opening with a great stone. They were troubled and could not leave Him alone.

One by one they prayed and then it is written that they recounted many stories of His kindness and His acts. But the night was cold and black and finally, weeping, they went away.

Death had not eased the hearts of the wicked Pharisees and they still worried over the words of Jesus when He said:

"After three days I rise again."

So they hastened to Pilate and urged that he act.

"Command that the sepulcher be made sure until the third day lest His Disciples come and steal Him away and say unto the people, 'He is risen from the dead.' And then the last error would be worse than the first."

Pilate answered:

"Ye have a guard; go, make it as sure as you can."

So the Pharisees and Scribes went by torchlight to the sepulcher protected by guards and in the chill night sealed the great stone.

And then they went to their homes and the Passover feast and the day of infamy was ended.

Day of resurrection

In the early hours of that Sabbath morn came a quake and the earth trembled and Jerusalem was troubled. Out of the skies as a lightning shaft came an angel in white raiment to the sepulcher where Jesus Christ lay buried. He rolled away the great stone and terrified guards fell as if dead.

And then the dawn was still and beautiful.

One by one the stars were doused and a morning carved from heaven broke over the countryside.

In great caution and sadness went Mary Magdalene and Mary of Bethany to the sepulcher to weep once more over their departed Master; perhaps to spread more spices over His body if the stone could be moved. But they were astonished and without words when they saw the stone had been rolled away.

Could His body have been stolen away in the night? Could He now lie in a common grave? The women moved closer and dared to enter. At first they saw nothing. Then a young man whose white garment shattered the tomb's darkness spoke:

"*Be not afraid. He is not here, for He is risen as He said.*"

Frightened, trembling, the women listened.

"*Go quickly and tell His Disciples that He is risen from the dead. And behold, He goeth before you into Galilee; there shall ye see Him.*"

Quickly the women fled to the house where His Disciples were in hiding and spread the news.

"*They have taken away The Lord out of the tomb, and we know not where they have laid Him.*"

Simon Peter and John heard and rushed from the house. John, the younger, came first to the sepulcher and looked past the opening. He saw linen cloth on the ground, but was fearful of entering.

Simon, breathless from his run, arrived and the two Disciples entered the tomb. True, the linens and the white napkin which had been folded around His head were there. And they departed in haste and returned to their house.

But Mary lingered and wept. She peered into the sepulcher and saw two angels sitting where His body had been. And they said:

"*Woman, why do you weep?*"

"*Because they have taken away my Lord and I know not where they have laid Him.*"

Then she turned to go away and Jesus stood nearby, but she did not know Him.

"*Woman,*" He said, "*why do you weep? Whom do you seek?*"

But Mary supposed Him to be the gardener and she said:

"*Sir, if you have taken Him away, tell me where you have laid Him and I will take Him away.*"

And Jesus said unto her:

"*Mary.*"

And she rejoiced and cried:

"Teacher!"

But He motioned her away and said:

"Touch Me not, for I am not yet ascended unto the Father. But go to My brethren and say to them, 'I ascend unto My Father, and your Father, and My God and your God.'"

Mary arose and rushed to the Disciples, exclaiming:

"I have seen The Lord."

The word spread and Matthew told that dazed guards reported the Resurrection to High Priests and Scribes. In hurried counsel with the Elders it was decided to give the guards much money and say unto them:

"If questioned, say 'His Disciples came by night and stole Him away while we slept.'"

Soon, two friends of Jesus who had been in the house with His Disciples, journeyed afoot to nearby Emmaus and were talking of events of the past few days in Jerusalem. A shadow fell across their path and they turned to see a stranger. He inquired of their conversation and they told Him the story of Jesus' suffering and the reports of His Resurrection. But of the last, they spoke in doubt.

And then the stranger started from Moses and quoted from all the Prophets in interpreting the Scriptures. Soon they arrived in Emmaus and He sat down with them to eat. He blessed the bread and breaking it gave it to them. The bread was broken!

In astonishment they looked and they knew it was He! And then He vanished. Straightway they returned to Jerusalem and burst into the house of the Disciples, saying:

"The Lord is risen indeed, and hath appeared to Simon!"

And while the eleven Disciples heard in wonderment, He appeared in the doorway. One by one He looked at them and then He said: *"Peace be unto you."*

The Disciples were frightened and feared they had seen a spirit.

"Why are ye troubled and why do questionings arise in your hearts? See My hands and feet, that it is I Myself. Handle Me and see, for a spirit hath not flesh and bones as ye behold Me having."

He lifted His hands and showed them His feet. The scars of Crucifixion were still there. He opened his garment and the mark of the spear was on His side.

In joy they still disbelieved, and He asked for meat. And He took it and ate. They believed.

"Peace be unto you. As the Father hath sent Me, even so send I you. Receive ye the Holy Spirit. Whosoever sins ye forgive, they are forgiven unto them. Whosoever sins ye retain, they are retained . . ."

They believed and went out to carry His gospel into every land.

And out of the heaven seemed to come words reminiscent of His baptism: *"This is My beloved Son in whom I am well pleased . . ."*

Designed and produced by Ben Feder Incorporated

Art Direction by Ben Feder

Artists: Edwin Schmidt and Emil Biemann

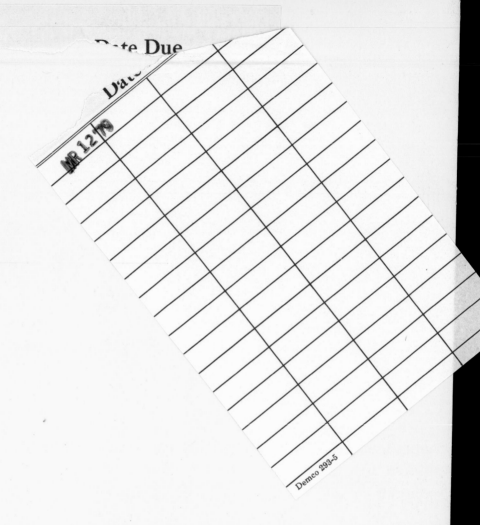

Date Due

Date

MR 12 79

Demco 293-5